Published by Authority of the
Minister of the Environment
Government of Canada

# Insects of Eastern Larch, Cedar and Juniper

A.H. Rose and
O.H. Lindquist

Great Lakes Forest Research
Centre
Sault Ste. Marie, Ontario,
P6A 5M7

Department of the Environment
Canadian Forestry Service
Forestry Technical Report 28
Ottawa, 1980

Available in Canada through
Authorized Bookstore Agents
and other bookstores

or by mail from

Canadian Government Publishing
Centre
Supply and Services Canada
Hull, Quebec, Canada K1A 0S9

Catalogue No. Fo64-28-1980
ISBN 0-660-10421-0

Canada: $6.95
Other countries: $8.35

Price subject to change without
notice.

Cette publication est également
disponible en français sous le
titre
*Insectes du mélèze, du thuya et
du genévrier de l'est du Canada.*

Printed in Canada

Other Canadian Forestry Service
handbooks in this series include:
*Insects of Eastern Pines
Insectes des pins de l'est
du Canada.*

*Insects of Eastern Spruces, Fir
and Hemlock
Insectes des épinettes, du sapin
et de la pruche de l'est du
Canada.*

# Abstract

# Résumé

This handbook is designed to enable people interested in trees to identify insects causing damage to them. All insect species or groups that have caused damage to larch, cedar and juniper in Canada east of the Rocky Mountains are included. About 80 species are treated and of these 43 are found on larch, 22 on cedar, and 16 on juniper. The insect and/or its damage can be identified by means of flow chart keys using non technical language along with some 150 colored illustrations. Biological sketches of the insect are given, and the need for control measures, along with the timing of application, is prescribed. Common names of insects are used generally, but the scientific names are also given in the text.

Ce manuel veut aider les gens qui portent intérêt aux arbres à identifier les insectes qui les endommagent. Il comprend toutes espèces ou tous groupes d'insectes qui ont endommagé le mélèze, le thuya et le genévrier canadiens à l'est des Rocheuses. Les auteurs étudient environ 80 espèces, dont 43 sur le mélèze, 22 sur le thuya et 16 sur le genévrier. Chaque espèce d'insecte et (ou) les dommages causés peuvent être identifiés au moyen d'un diagramme-clé facile à comprendre et par environ 150 illustrations en couleurs. À ceci s'ajoutent la description sommaire biologique de l'insecte et les mesures de lutte incluant le temps de leur application. En général, les auteurs identifient les insectes par leur nom commun, mais le nom scientifique (latin) est aussi donné dans le texte.

# Foreword

This is the third in a series of handbooks that is capturing the attention of forest managers, pest extension people, and those of the general public interested in the maintenance of healthy trees. This publication completes coverage of the major insects of coniferous trees in eastern Canada. As with *Insects of Eastern Pines* and *Insects of Eastern Spruces, Fir and Hemlock* much information was drawn from the data base developed over many years by the Forest Insect and Disease Survey. Particular mention again is made of contributing specialists at Canadian Forestry Service Research Centres across the country, taxonomists at the Biosystematics Research Institute, Agriculture Canada, Ottawa, and dedicated field and laboratory staff of the Survey. The authors continue to challenge the task of preparing and presenting an enormous amount of information in a concise, attractive, and useful form.

W.L. Sippell
Program Manager,
Entomology and Pathology

# Contents

Eastern larch

Eastern white cedar

Common juniper

Eastern red cedar

Creeping juniper

# Introduction

This handbook completes the series dealing with the insects of conifers in central and eastern Canada and adjacent areas of the United States. Earlier handbooks in this Canadian Forestry Service series are *Insects of Eastern Pines,* Publication 1313, and *Insects of Eastern Spruces, Fir and Hemlock,* Forestry Technical Report 23. Information for this edition, as for the others, was drawn mainly from data and material accumulated over a 30-year period by the Forest Insect and Disease Survey of Ontario. However, additional information has been drawn from reports and publications of Survey Units in other provinces as well as from the entomological literature. All insects that have caused injury in the past are included, and about 80 species or species groups are treated.

The format of this handbook differs from the earlier ones as shown in the table of contents. In this text it was found necessary to treat each species of tree separately since the insect complex on each one is for the most part different. However, where insects feed on more than one tree species they are included in each appropriate key, but the reader is referred to a single write-up in one of the sections. Flowcharts are used to facilitate the identification of insects or insect injury, and biological information is provided for all species. For some species it was not possible to provide information on the seasonal occurrence of various stages over broad areas. However,

Ontario data, usually given, may be used as a guide for other areas. References in the text to colored illustrations are indicated by the symbol □. For the identification of any insect on larch, cedar, or juniper not treated here, a representative sample of living specimens and damage should be forwarded to the Forest Insect and Disease Survey at the appropriate Research Centre serving your area (see map on page 10).

## Injury
Injury to trees can be caused by such varied factors as climate, insects, mites, diseases, birds, and mammals. Man often causes injury by mechanical means or by adversely altering the tree's environment either above or below ground. With a few exceptions, this handbook deals with problems created by insects or mites.

All parts of a tree are subject to attack by some insect species. The degree of injury inflicted, however, depends on the number of insects, type of feeding, time of year, and how vital to survival is the part attacked.

## Control
Because the kinds of pesticide that can be used are constantly changing as unacceptable side effects are discovered, no specific control measures are given in this handbook. However, the necessity for control and the stages in the pest's life cycle most susceptible to control measures are indicated. Also, to facilitate selection, the re-

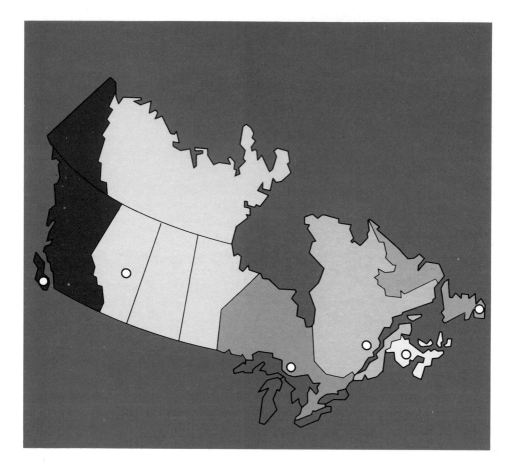

Forest Research Centres

Pacific Forest Research Centre
506 West Burnside Road, Victoria, British Columbia V8Z 1M5

Northern Forest Research Centre
5320-122 Street, Edmonton, Alberta T5J 3S5

Great Lakes Forest Research Centre
Box 490, Sault Ste. Marie, Ontario P6A 5M7

Laurentian Forest Research Centre
Box 3800, Ste. Foy, Quebec G1V 4C7

Maritimes Forest Research Centre
Box 4000, Fredericton, New Brunswick E3B 5G4

Newfoundland Forest Research Centre
Box 6028, Building 304, St. John's, Newfoundland A1C 5X8

quired type of pesticide (contact, stomach, systemic, or fumigant) is given. Information on currently registered pesticides may be obtained from various government agencies and is available also on the label of the pesticide container. If large-scale chemical control measures are necessary, the advice of a specialist should be obtained.

**Further Reading**
Historical information on important or noteworthy forest insects in Canada may be found in publications issued by the Canadian Forestry Service of the Department of the Environment. These include the Annual Reports of the Forest Insect and Disease Survey, the four-volume report on Forest Lepidoptera of Canada, and *Aerial Control of Forest Insects in Canada,* M.L. Prebble, editor. *Eastern Forest Insects,* by W.L. Baker, 1972, Miscellaneous Publication 1175 of the Forest Service of the United States Department of Agriculture, is a comprehensive treatment of the subject and contains an extensive list of references to papers in entomology journals. A more recent publication, *Insects That Feed on Trees and Shrubs,* by W.T. Johnson and H.H. Lyon, 1976, is also recommended. For more detailed information on insects in this field, a specialist in forest entomology should be consulted.

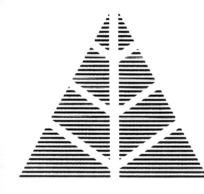

# Eastern larch

Tree in winter

Tree in fall

Male flower

Female flower

The distribution of eastern larch, *Larix laricina* (Du Roi) K. Koch, also called tamarack and hackmatack depending on where you live, extends from the Mackenzie River Valley east to the Atlantic Ocean. Formerly, the wood was used extensively because of its resistance to decay, but for various reasons its use has declined greatly in recent years. Members of this genus, unlike the other conifers that retain their needles for a number of years, drop their needles annually □. Late in the fall, after the broad-leaved trees have lost their foliage, larch needles turn yellow □ and are usually shed before much snow has fallen. Introduced species, of European and Asian origin, are commonly planted in reforestation programs. They can be readily distinguished from the native species by their larger cone: cones of eastern larch are about 12 mm long.

Some shoots on larch are elongated, but most are dwarf □. Needles on elongated shoots are ar-

Elongated and dwarf shoots

New cone

Old cone

# Eastern white cedar

ranged in a long spiral, whereas those on dwarf shoots are in dense whorls. In the spring, needles on dwarf shoots are well developed before the elongating shoots become evident. The dark brown buds are located at the tip and along the side of elongated shoots, and at the tip of dwarf shoots. The male □ and female □ flowers also arise on dwarf shoots. The upright cones □ mature and shed their seed in the year of development. The open cones □ remain on the tree over winter.

Eastern white cedar, *Thuja occidentalis* L., often called arbor-vitae, especially when it is used as an ornamental □, occurs from Manitoba to New Brunswick and in parts of Nova Scotia. There are a large number of forms of cedar including pyramidal, globose, and pendulous ones that have been cultivated for ornamental purposes. Cedar wood is soft, light, and resistant to decay. There are three leaf shapes. Two of these are short and wide and are arranged in

Ornamental cedar

opposite pairs clasping the shoots to form flat fan-shaped sprays of foliage □. The third shape is long and narrow □ and is found on vigorous shoots: in succeeding years these leaves turn brown and are cast off, leaving the orange-brown twig exposed. The inconspicuous male and female flowers are located at the tip of the shoots. The pale green immature cones □ turn brown by fall, remain over winter, and shed their seeds in the spring □.

New cones

Leaf shapes

Open cones

# Juniper

There are three kinds of junipers in the *Juniperus* L. genus in eastern Canada. Two are widely distributed shrubs. The common juniper of abandoned farms, having prickly needles with a white upper surface □, is better known than the creeping juniper, which has soft needles and is found mainly on sandy or rocky soil. The third juniper, generally called eastern red cedar, *J. virginiana* L., is a small tree. In Canada, it has a limited distribution, mostly in Ontario, with small pockets in Quebec, and makes its best growth in soils of limestone origin. Junipers have two kinds of leaves: scale-like leaves □ that are arranged in four rows covering the twigs to form four-sided branchlets; needle-like leaves □ that are near the tip of vigorous shoots. Unlike most other conifers, junipers usually bear their male and female flowers on different trees. The male flowers □ arise at the tips of branchlets. The fruit, initially pale green with a white bloom but turning blue-black □ as it ripens, is berry-like and requires one to three seasons before the seeds mature. A large number of forms of eastern red cedar have been cultivated for ornamental plantings.

Common juniper leaves

Eastern red cedar needles (mature)

Eastern red cedar male flowers

Common juniper male flowers

Eastern red cedar fruit

Eastern red cedar needles (juvenile)

# Types of insects

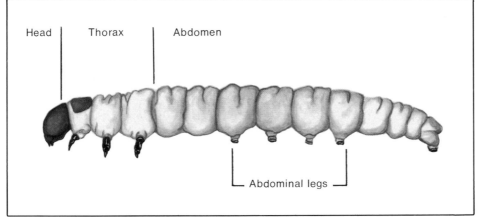

Will be a moth

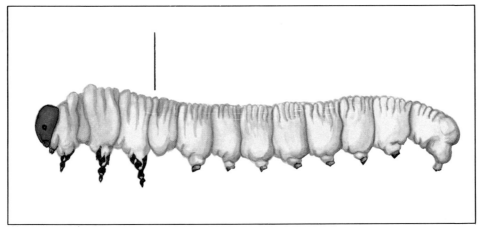

Will be a sawfly

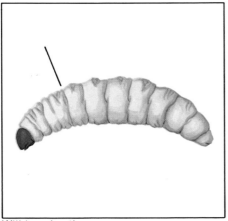

Will be a beetle

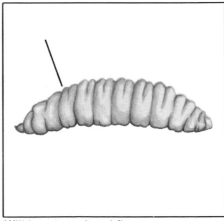

Will be a two-winged fly

Most of our destructive forest insects develop through four stages – egg, larva, pupa, and adult – each distinctly different from the other. The larva, sometimes referred to as "caterpillar," "worm," "grub," or "maggot," is the principal feeding stage. It sheds its skin at intervals as it grows, from the tiny individual that emerges from the egg to the full-grown larva. The pupa is an inactive transformation stage between the feeding larva and the reproducing adult. Larvae, particularly those destined to become moths, vary greatly in color, shape, and size, and may be hairy or naked. Most of our forest insects can be grouped according to the general structure of the larvae as illustrated in the simplified outline drawings □.

A few of our forest insects develop through only three stages – egg, nymph □, and adult. In this type of development the nymph also sheds its skin at intervals as it grows, but, unlike the larva, it resembles the adult and does not require a pupal stage in which to change to an adult insect.

Since adults of most injurious insects discussed in this handbook are seldom seen, they are not included here. A number of them, however, are illustrated elsewhere.

The mites □, minute relatives of spiders, are not technically insects, since the adults have either two or four pairs of legs, whereas insect adults have three pairs of legs. Young mites generally resemble the adult and there is no pupal stage.

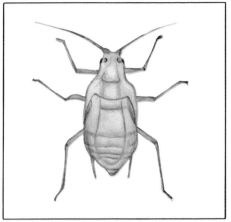

Aphid nymph

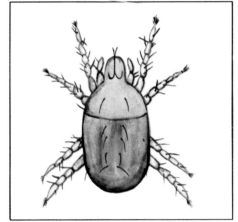

Mite

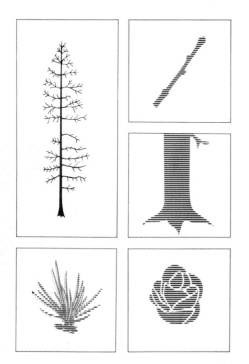

Pages 24 to 66 show how to identify insects on or injury to various
parts of a larch tree.

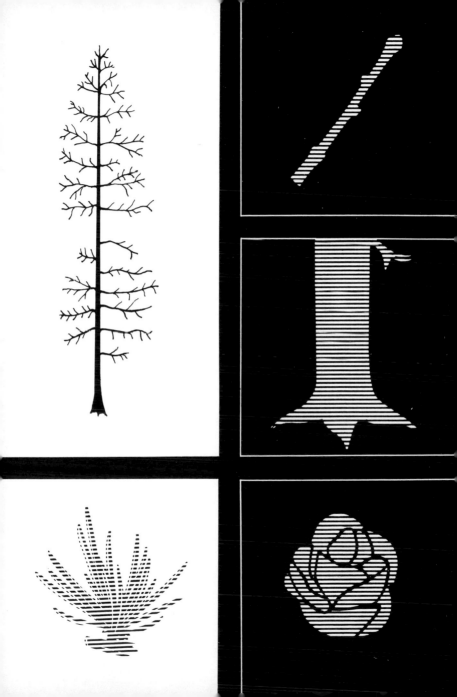

# **Larch** – needle

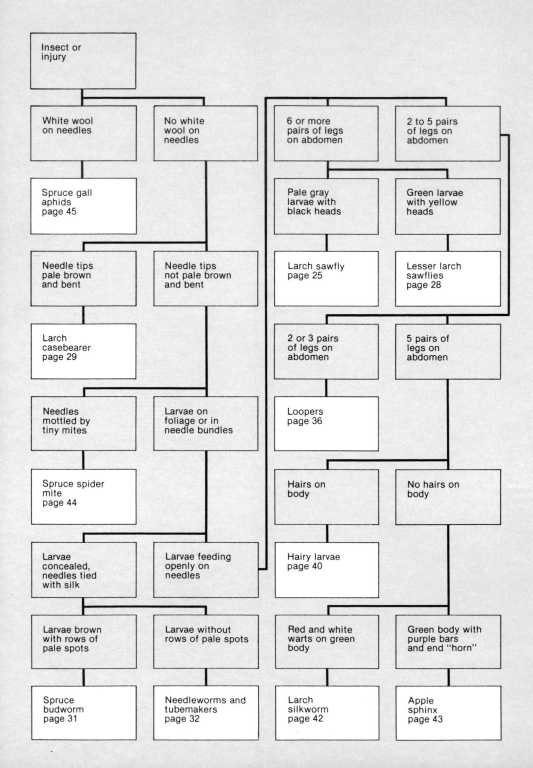

| | | | |
|---|---|---|---|
| Insect or injury | | | |
| White wool on needles | No white wool on needles | 6 or more pairs of legs on abdomen | 2 to 5 pairs of legs on abdomen |
| Spruce gall aphids page 45 | | Pale gray larvae with black heads | Green larvae with yellow heads |
| Needle tips pale brown and bent | Needle tips not pale brown and bent | Larch sawfly page 25 | Lesser larch sawflies page 28 |
| Larch casebearer page 29 | | 2 or 3 pairs of legs on abdomen | 5 pairs of legs on abdomen |
| Needles mottled by tiny mites | Larvae on foliage or in needle bundles | Loopers page 36 | |
| Spruce spider mite page 44 | | Hairs on body | No hairs on body |
| Larvae concealed, needles tied with silk | Larvae feeding openly on needles | Hairy larvae page 40 | |
| Larvae brown with rows of pale spots | Larvae without rows of pale spots | Red and white warts on green body | Green body with purple bars and end "horn" |
| Spruce budworm page 31 | Needleworms and tubemakers page 32 | Larch silkworm page 42 | Apple sphinx page 43 |

# Larch sawfly

The larch sawfly, *Pristiphora erichsonii* (Hartig), is a serious pest of larch in North America. Its origin has been debated by entomologists for many years. However, intensive studies now indicate a number of strains, some native and others introduced. Epidemics occur periodically across Canada and the northern United States and the absence of mature stands is often attributed to tree mortality caused by past infestations of this pest. The larvae feed on the needles of native and exotic European, Japanese, and Siberian larches. The adult sawflies display a remarkable ability to find isolated ornamental trees far removed from stands of larch.

There is one generation each year with full-grown larvae overwintering in cocoons in the ground. In spring or summer the larvae change to pupae, although a small proportion of the population may remain as larvae in their cocoons for two or three winters. The pupae change to adult sawflies □ over an extended period from May to August, depending on site and climatic conditions. Males seldom exceed 2 percent of the adult population, and reproduction for the most part occurs without fertilization of the female.

The average number of eggs laid by a female is about 75. Usually 10 to 30 eggs are laid in any one shoot, in a double row of slits cut along one side of the elongating shoot □. When egg slits are cut early in the growing season the shoots tend to curl in a characteris-

Adult (greatly enlarged)

Mature larva

Curled shoot

Eggs in shoot

Cocoon

Colony of larvae

tic manner □. The larvae are grayish with black heads. They feed in groups □ from June to September, stripping the needle clusters from whole branches and often from the entire tree. When full grown and about 20 mm long, the larvae □ drop to the ground and spin tough, oval, silken cocoons in the litter □ where they overwinter.

Populations of the larch sawfly are regulated by many natural factors including parasites, predators, disease, and flooding of cocoon sites. The predator *Apateticus bracteatus* Fitch □ is one of a number of stink bugs preying on larvae, and a species of the fungus *Entomophthora* causes the death of others □. Shrews and voles are important predators during the cocoon stage. In fact, shrews have been introduced into Newfoundland to improve the natural control of the sawfly there. Elsewhere in Canada, a number of parasites have been introduced from Europe with some success in regulating sawfly populations. If chemical control measures are required, an insecticide recommended for sawflies should be applied against young feeding larvae as they appear throughout the summer.

Stinkbug predator

Larva killed by fungus

# Lesser larch sawflies

*A. luteipes* larva

The lesser larch sawflies of the genus *Anoplonyx* occur from Alberta to Newfoundland and in the northeastern United States. There are two species in this area: *A. luteipes* (Cresson) is the common one and *A. canadensis* Harrington is found less often. No serious injury to larch by the larvae of these sawflies has been recorded.

The adults emerge from overwintering cocoons in the spring and the females lay their eggs, usually singly, in the needles. The larvae tend to be solitary feeders and may be found on the foliage from about mid-June to early October. The larvae of the two species are similar in color and markings except that *luteipes* has three, often indistinct, grayish lines on each side of the body □ whereas *canadensis* has one lateral line on each side. When full grown the larvae are about 13 mm long. They overwinter in cocoons in the soil and change to pupae in the spring.

No control measures have been required for these insects.

# Larch casebearer

Damaged needles

The larch casebearer, *Coleophora laricella* (Hübner), is an introduced pest that was first found on this continent in the 1880s and now occurs from Newfoundland and the Maritime Provinces to south-eastern Manitoba. It is also found in the Rocky Mountain region of southern British Columbia and across the border in adjacent areas of the United States. It is often a serious defoliator of both native and exotic species of larch. When the insect is abundant, needle-mining by the larvae causes the tips of needles to bend and turn light brown □.

Larch casebearer adults □ are tiny moths that fly from late May to August. The eggs are laid on the needles and hatching occurs in two weeks. The larvae bore into the needles, which they mine until late summer. At this time the larva lines a hollowed portion of the needle with silk and then chews the section free at both ends. The resulting case □ becomes a portable shelter for the rest of the larval period. In feeding, the larva fastens the fore-end of the case to a needle, which it then mines as far as it can reach. Winter is spent in the case, which is fastened with silk to a twig, usually at the base of a bud. Feeding is resumed in early spring when the new needles appear, and more needles are mined for three to four weeks. The larva changes to a pupa in the case, which has been fastened with silk to a needle or twig. The pupa soon changes to a moth to complete the

Adult

Larval cases

life cycle.

A number of species of parasites have been imported from Europe to combat the casebearer, and two of these, *Agathis pumila* (Ratzeburg) and *Chrysocharis laricinellae* (Ratzeburg), are now widely established on this continent. These two species are believed to be the causes of the reduction in outbreak severity in eastern North America. If chemical control is necessary, a systemic insecticide applied in early spring should be effective.

# Spruce budworm

Full-grown larva

The spruce budworm, *Choristo-neura fumiferana* (Clemens), is a highly destructive pest in the spruce-fir forests of North America and, when large numbers are present, severe feeding damage also occurs on other conifers such as larch.

The larvae feed on the needles from early spring to July, usually spinning fine silk about the needles □. When the larva is full grown □, and about 22 mm long, it changes to a pupa on the foliage. The gray to reddish moths fly from late June to early August. Further information on this insect may be found in *Insects of Eastern Spruces, Fir and Hemlock,* Forestry Technical Report 23, an earlier handbook in this series.

On shade or ornamental trees, damage by the budworm can be kept to a minimum by the application of a contact or stomach insecticide while the larvae are still small.

Damage

# Needleworms and tubemakers

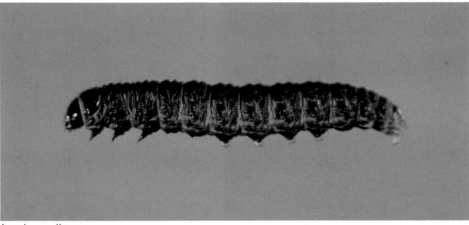

Larch needleworm

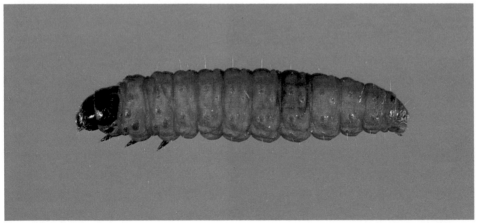

Brown larch tubemaker

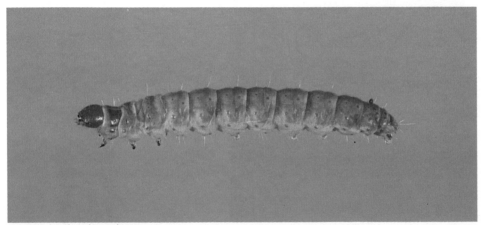

Orange larch tubemaker

- Larvae dusky...........Larch needleworm
- Larvae brown..........Brown larch tubemaker
- Larvae orange.........Orange larch tubemaker

The larch needleworm, *Zeiraphera improbana* (Walker), is distributed across southern Canada and the northern United States. It is usually present in low numbers, but occasional epidemics, usually of short duration, have occurred on native larch in Newfoundland, Quebec, Ontario, and British Columbia. Although larch is the primary host, young spruce understory trees may also be severely defoliated.

The adults of the needleworm, small dark gray moths, are in flight during July or August in Ontario. The eggs □ are usually laid in clusters deep in the current year's cones, where they overwinter. The eggs hatch and the young larvae begin feeding in late April or May, when the new needle clusters on dwarf twigs are about 3 mm long. The larvae, cream with black heads, feed singly, and are later found in clusters of needles tied with silk to form compact tubes □. When the larvae are full grown □, usually in July, they are dusky blackish and about 14 mm long. They hide in ragged shelters of dead needles tied with silk along the twig □ from which they feed on nearby foliage. These larvae soon drop from the trees and change to pupae in silk-lined cocoons in the ground litter. The adults emerge later in summer.

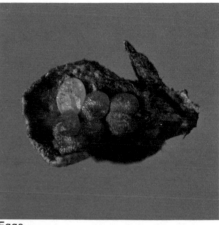

Eggs

Early larva in tube

Damage

Tube of needles

Pupa in tube

Since infestations of the larch needleworm have been of short duration, no large-scale control measures have been required. However, a contact or stomach pesticide, applied when new needles appear, should be effective against this pest. In Ontario, the braconid parasite, *Clinocentrus* species, is apparently an important biological control agent.

The brown larch tubemaker, *Spilonota lariciana* Heinemann, now occurring from the Great Lakes to the Atlantic seaboard, is probably an introduced species. In southern Ontario it is often common in plantations of European larch. Because serious injury has not been recorded, no control measures have been required to date.

The life history of this insect in North America is not well known. In Ontario, the gray-patterned moths fly in June. The young larvae feed in tubes of needles tied with silk from July to late fall and presumably overwinter in hibernacula on the trees. In the spring the larvae tie new tubes of needles □ in which they feed until full grown □ (see page 32), when they are about 12 mm long. The larvae change to pupae □ in the needle-tubes on the trees from May to mid-June.

The orange larch tubemaker, *Pulicalvaria laricis* Freeman, is a species that is relatively new to science. It was described and named from Ontario specimens in 1965. The larvae have been found only in small number in various parts of Ontario.

Pupa exposed in tube

Empty pupal case

# Loopers

In its adult stage the tubemaker is a tiny moth that usually flies in early summer. The eggs are laid on or near the foliage. On hatching, the larvae tunnel into needles where they feed until the fall. At the onset of cold weather the larvae hibernate in shelters of a few needles and excreta tied along the twig. In the spring they tie clusters of needles together to form bundles or tubes in which they complete their feeding, usually by mid-June. The full-grown larva □ (see page 32) is about 8 mm long. It changes to a dark-coloured pupa □ in the final feeding tube or in a newly constructed one. When the moth emerges the empty pupal case typically protrudes from the tube □.

No control measures have been required to date.

Many kinds of loopers occur on larch in eastern Canada, but they are usually found singly or in small numbers and no serious injury is recorded. Most species are general feeders on a variety of coniferous and deciduous trees. Five of the more common ones that feed on larch are illustrated.

The larch looper, *Semiothisa sexmaculata* (Packard), is found from eastern British Columbia to Newfoundland throughout most of the range of larch. The larvae feed in July, August and September, and have a light □ and a dark color phase □. When full grown and about 18 mm long they drop to the ground, where they change to pupae and overwinter in the soil. The closely related species *S. oweni* (Swett) and *S. signaria dispuncta* (Walker) also occur on larch.

The hemlock looper □, *Lambdina fiscellaria fiscellaria* (Guenée), is a serious pest of balsam fir and hemlock from Ontario to Newfoundland and in the northeastern United States. It is a general feeder and has been reported to defoliate larch. The larvae feed from June to September, but mainly in July, and attain a length of about 30 mm. Detailed information on this species may be found in *Insects of Eastern Spruces, Fir and Hemlock,* Forestry Technical Report 23, an earlier handbook in this series.

The saddleback looper □, *Ectropis crepuscularia* (Denis and Schifermüller), is another general feeder. Although of no consequence in central and eastern Canada it has on occasion caused tree mortality

Larch looper (dark phase)

Larch looper (light phase)

Hemlock looper

Saddleback looper

to western hemlock and other coniferous and deciduous trees in British Columbia. The larvae feed from June to September and are about 32 mm long when full grown. This insect overwinters as a pupa in the soil.

The chainspotted geometer □, *Cingilia catenaria* (Drury), feeds on a wide variety of trees and ground-cover plants and is occasionally abundant on larch in eastern Canada and the northeastern United States. The larvae feed from June to August. When full grown they are about 45 mm long. Winter is spent in the egg stage.

The pepper-and-salt moth, *Biston cognataria* (Guenée), feeds on a variety of trees and shrubs, including larch, across Canada and the northern United States. The larvae □ feed mainly from July to early September and are about 45 mm long when full grown. No serious injury to trees by this looper has been reported to date.

Other loopers only occasionally found on larch are illustrated in *Insects of Eastern Spruces, Fir and Hemlock,* Forestry Technical Report 23, an earlier handbook in this series. These species are the false hemlock looper, *Nepytia canosaria* (Walker); the fringed looper, *Campaea perlata* Guenée; the diamond-backed looper, *Hypagyrtis piniata* Packard; the spruce-and-fir looper, *Semiothisa signaria dispuncta* (Walker); the yellowlined conifer looper, *Nyctobia limitaria* Walker; the dashlined looper, *Protoboarmia porcelaria indicataria* Walker; the spruce looper, *Caripeta divisata* Walker; and species of *Eupithecia.*

Control measures for loopers on larch are not usually required. If large numbers occur on shade trees, a contact or stomach insecticide recommended for caterpillars should be applied before the larvae are full grown.

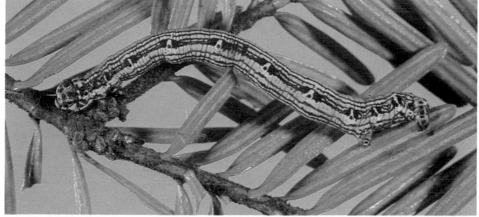

Chainspotted geometer

Photo credit, Laurentian Forest Research Centre

Pepper-and-salt moth looper

# Hairy larvae

Rusty tussock moth larva

Whitemarked tussock moth larva

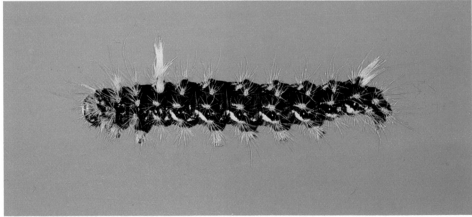
Tufted caterpillar

Two tussock moths, whose larvae occasionally feed on larch, occur commonly on deciduous and coniferous trees from Alberta to Newfoundland and in the northern United States. Larvae of the rusty tussock moth □, *Orgyia antiqua* (Linnaeus), feed throughout June, July, and August. When full grown and about 28 mm long, they spin yellow-gray cocoons of silk and hair in a variety of niches on the tree or on other objects. The larvae subsequently change to pupae in the cocoons. The adults, winged males and wingless females, emerge mainly in August and September. The female lays her eggs in a single-layered mass on the cocoon from which she emerged. The eggs hatch the following spring.

The life history of the whitemarked tussock moth, *O. leucostigma* (J.E. Smith), is similar to that of the preceding species. However, the larvae are not usually found on conifers outside of the Maritimes. The full-grown larva □ is about 35 mm long.

The tufted caterpillar, *Panthea acronyctoides* (Walker), occurs in small numbers on conifers, from Alberta to Newfoundland and in the northeastern United States. The larvae feed from July to early September and when full grown □ are about 34 mm long.

The hairskirted caterpillar, *Tolype laricis* (Fitch), is found, usually in small numbers, from British Columbia to Nova Scotia and in the eastern United States. Feeding larvae, found mainly in July and

Hairskirted caterpillar

August, are about 35 mm long when full grown □.

A virus disease and parasites have helped to terminate epidemics of the whitemarked tussock moth in the Maritimes. For valuable ornamental trees and in plantations, a contact or stomach insecticide registered for use against these hairy caterpillars should be applied when the larvae are young to control any of the four species mentioned.

# Larch silkworm

Larch silkworm                                                    Photo credit, L. Kohalmi

The larch silkworm, *Hyalophora columbia* (S. I. Smith), is unique in that it is the only member of the family of giant silkworms that feeds on a conifer. It occurs in southern Canada and the northern United States, in a narrow band from southeastern Manitoba and northern Wisconsin to Nova Scotia and Maine. Although this is one of the largest forest insects in Canada, it is relatively rare and there is no record of it causing serious injury to larch.

The pea green larvae have prominent warts, feed in July and August, and attain a length of about 76 mm when full grown □. They spin relatively small, silken, spindle-shaped cocoons that are dark brown with silvery striations, and are usually attached to the host tree. The larvae change to pupae inside the cocoons and overwinter there. The adults fly from May to July.

Since this beautiful moth □ is rarely seen there is an impression that it is becoming extinct. Regard-

Moth (greatly reduced)

less of the validity of the impression, it should become a protected species and its feeding on larch should be an acceptable price to pay for its presence.

# Apple sphinx

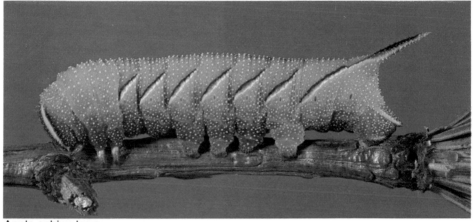

Apple sphinx larva

The apple sphinx, *Sphinx gordius* Cramer, is found over a wide area of Canada and the United States east of the Rocky Mountains. It has not caused serious injury to larch but is included here because of its striking appearance and wide distribution. The larvae feed from mid-July to late September and are about 48 mm long when full grown ☐. There is one generation each year and the insect overwinters as a pupa in the soil. The adults are known as hawk moths or hummingbird moths, and fly from May to July. Because of their size and their habit of collecting nectar from deep-throated flowers, they may be mistaken for hummingbirds.

Because this larva feeds on a variety of plants ranging from shrubs and fruit trees to conifers it is not a rare insect, and damage to larch is of little consequence. So, rather than being considered an enemy as many of our forest insects are, this striking larva should be viewed as an interesting and colorful part of our environment.

# Spruce spider mite

The spruce spider mite, *Oligony-chus ununguis* (Jacobi), is often a serious pest on planted spruce and coniferous hedges. It is occasionally found in large numbers on larch, where feeding by the tiny mites causes a mottled discoloration of the needles □.

This mite overwinters in the egg stage on the twigs □. The eggs hatch in early spring. The mites feed by sucking sap from needles or shoots and spin fine silk as they move about on the foliage. They have an oval shape and vary in color from dark green to dark brown. When full grown they are about 0.5 mm long. Five to eight generations of mites may develop before the onset of cold weather in the fall. Further information on this species may be found in *Insects of Eastern Spruces, Fir and Hemlock,* Forestry Technical Report 23, an earlier handbook in this series.

If chemical control measures become necessary, a pesticide effective against mites should be used.

Discolored needles

Eggs

## Spruce gall aphids

Two common spruce gall aphids, *Adelges lariciatus* (Patch) and *A. strobilobius* (Kaltenbach), feed in alternate years on spruce and larch. They have complex life cycles and six generations usually occur in the two-year cycle □. Winged adults, about 2 mm long, occur only in the generation that moves from one kind of host tree to the other. In addition, two other little-known species of *Adelges* have been found in larch cones.

On larch, *A. lariciatus* is sometimes conspicuous because of the white wool □ which is produced by the feeding aphids on the damaged needles. Other generations of these aphids occur on twigs □ and in cones □.

Serious injury to larch by spruce gall aphids has not been recorded. However, if an abundance of aphids and white wool should appear on ornamental trees, they should be treated with a systemic pesticide.

Needle damage

Female and eggs

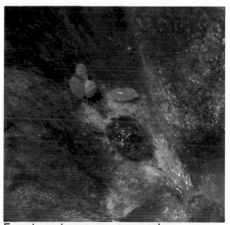
Female and eggs on cone scale

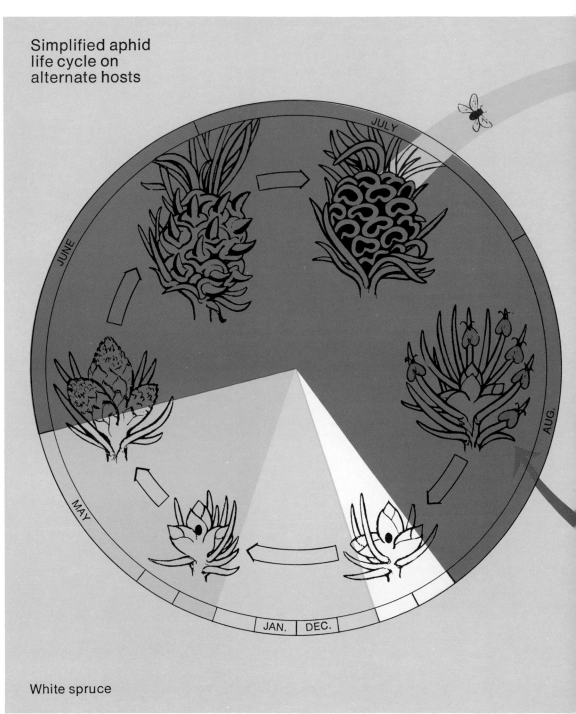

Simplified aphid
life cycle on
alternate hosts

JULY

JUNE

AUG.

MAY

JAN. DEC.

White spruce

Two-year life cycle

Eastern larch

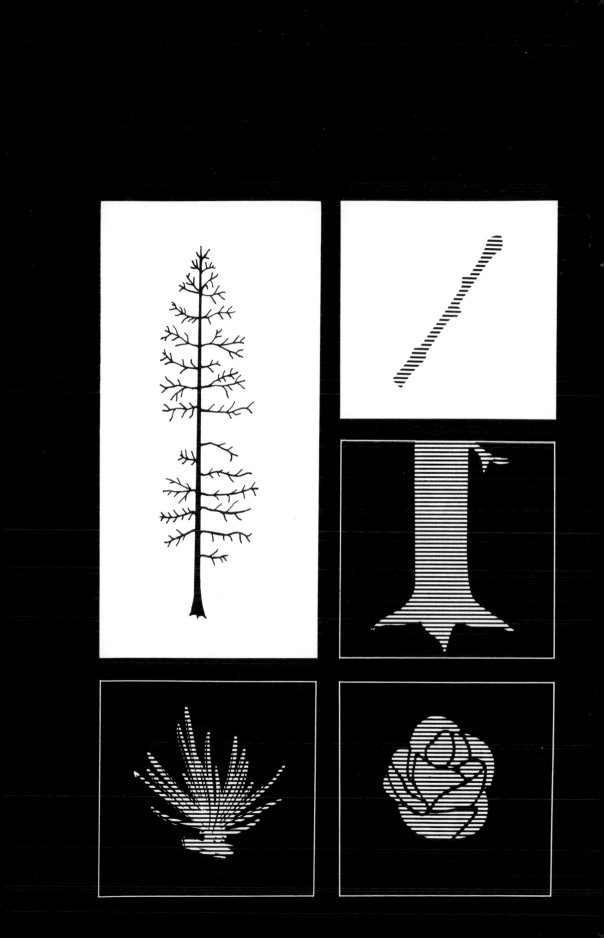

# **Larch –** shoot or twig

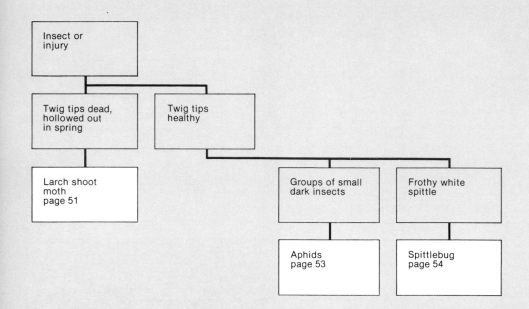

Insect or injury

Twig tips dead, hollowed out in spring

Twig tips healthy

Larch shoot moth
page 51

Groups of small dark insects

Frothy white spittle

Aphids
page 53

Spittlebug
page 54

# Larch shoot moth

Damaged tip in spring

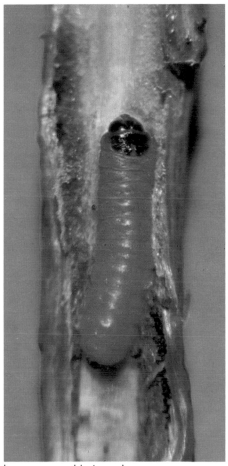

Larva exposed in tunnel

The larch shoot moth, *Argyresthia laricella* Kearfott, probably occurs throughout the range of the native larches in North America, and in southern Ontario it is often abundant in plantations of European larch. The larvae mine the shoots of host trees, but damaged tips □ do not become evident until the following year. Serious injury, however, is unusual.

The small pale moths □ fly from late May to August, depending on the climatic zone involved. The eggs are laid singly, usually at the base of a new shoot. The newly hatched larva enters the new shoot near its base and tunnels in the shoot throughout the summer and fall. In late fall the nearly full-grown larva lines the end of its tunnel with silk and overwinters there □. Feeding is resumed during mild periods throughout the winter. The larva completes its feeding in early spring and attains a length of about 7 mm. After cutting an exit hole and covering it with silk, the

Pupa in tunnel

larva changes to a pupa in a silk-lined chamber in the tunnel ☐, from late April to early July. The pupa changes to a moth after about 24 days. The moth emerges from the dead twig tip through the silk-covered exit hole cut by the larva.

Populations of the larch shoot moth are usually kept in check by parasites and birds, and large-scale control measures have not been required. On ornamental trees, the infested dead twig tips should be clipped and destroyed in early spring as soon as the new foliage appears.

Moth

## Aphids

A number of species of aphids of the genus *Cinara* live on larch in North America but serious feeding injury is unknown. The aphids pierce the bark with their long feeding tubes and suck sap from shoots, twigs, branches, stem or roots. They live in colonies □ and are usually attended by ants, which feed on the droplets of excreted liquid. These aphids vary in color from gray to brown or black and are less than 5 mm long □. All species overwinter in the egg stage. The eggs are blackish and are laid on the bark of twigs near buds □. Six generations in one year are not unusual in Canada, and succeeding generations often move to new sites on the tree as the season progresses. The life cycle is complex. For example, adults of the intermediate summer generations consist of females only, some winged and others wingless, both of which produce tiny nymphs rather than eggs. Males occur only in the late fall generation, which produces the overwintering eggs.

Control measures for these aphids have not been required in the forest. When control on ornamentals is necessary, a contact insecticide would be appropriate.

Colony

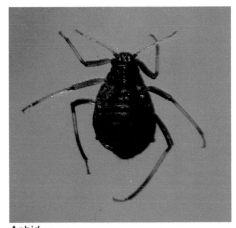
Aphid

Eggs

# Spittlebug

Spittle mass

The spittlebug, *Aphrophora cribrata* (Walker), formerly called *A. parallela* occurs throughout central and eastern Canada and the eastern United States. It feeds on many conifers but is of concern primarily in pine plantations. Although it is occasionally found on larch, serious feeding injury to that host is unknown. From May to July, one or more immature spittlebugs may be found under each frothy mass of spittle □, formed as they feed on the tree's sap. Control, if necessary, requires a contact insecticide applied in June with sufficient force to penetrate the spittle mass. Additional information on this insect may be found in *Insects of Eastern Pines,* Canadian Forestry Service Publication 1313, an earlier handbook in this series.

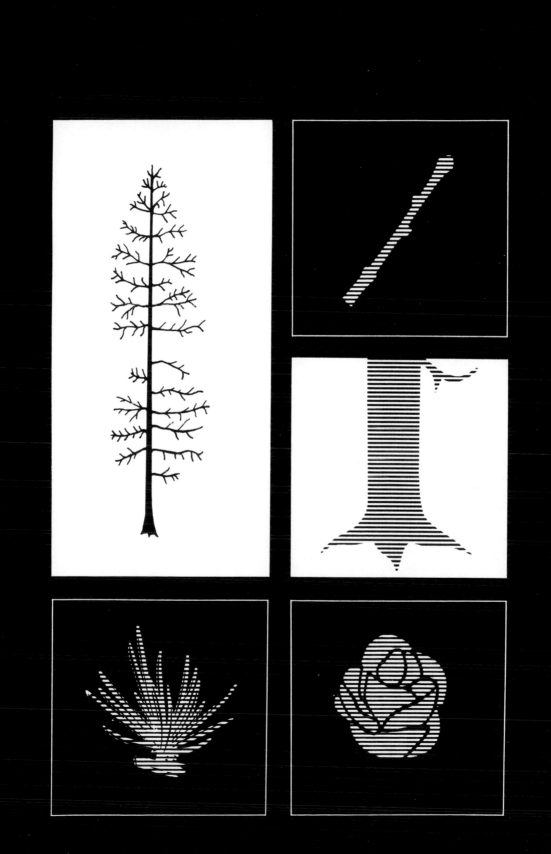

# **Larch –** stem or log

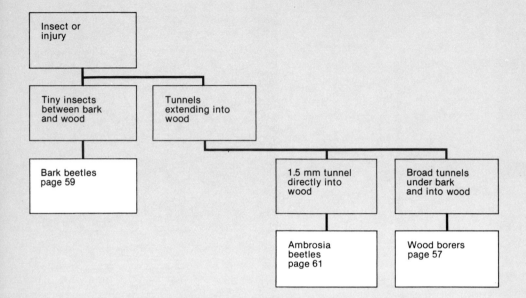

# Wood borers

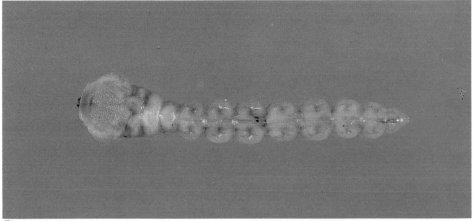

Flatheaded borer larva

Wood borers breed in recently dead or dying trees and usually become abundant in storm- or flood-damaged timber, in decadent forests, or where extensive harvesting operations have been carried out. The larvae tunnel in the wood and cause undesirable "worm-holes" in some wood products.

There are two common groups of wood borers in larch. The round-headed borers often tunnel deeply in the wood, whereas the flatheaded borers make shallow tunnels and are generally considered less damaging. The normal two-year life cycle of both groups is essentially the same. They usually pass the second winter as mature larvae at the end of a tunnel in the wood and change to the pupal and then to the adult stage in the spring. The adults emerge in early summer and, after feeding for a short while, seek recently dead or dying trees, and lay their eggs in the bark or under bark scales. The larvae, on hatching, tunnel through the bark

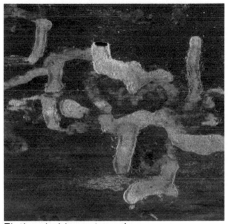

Flatheaded borer tunnel

and feed at the interface of wood and bark, lightly scoring the wood surface in the first summer. The boring dust and excrement, which may be relatively loose or tightly packed, and the characteristic tunnels constructed by the larvae, are often indicative of the species group involved.

The shallow, tortuous tunnel with tightly packed boring dust and a relatively flat larval entrance hole □ in the wood is characteristic of a flatheaded borer larva □,

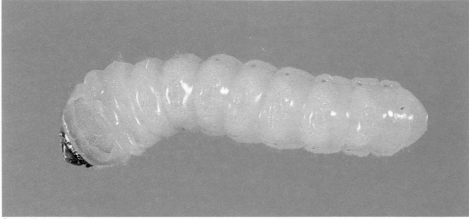
Roundheaded borer larva

such as *Chrysobothris* species. On the other hand, the deeply scored wood, a more compact tunnel, and coarse boring dust, with a more oval-shaped larval entrance in the wood ☐ are typical of second-year feeding by a roundheaded borer larva ☐ such as the white-spotted sawyer, *Monochamus scutellatus* Say. Adult sawyer beetles feed on the bark of living trees and often cause the death of twigs and branches. Additional information on wood borers will be found in *Insects of Eastern Spruces, Fir and Hemlock,* Forestry Technical Report 23, an earlier handbook in this series.

Roundheaded borer tunnel

are probably already doomed.

For information on the control of borers in logs, it would be advisable to consult the appropriate Research Centre listed on page 10. Kiln drying will kill tunnelling larvae in lumber. Adults emerging from logs or lumber will not attack the material again. Control of borers in stems of damaged or dying larch used as shade trees is seldom warranted, because the trees

# Bark beetles

Four-eyed spruce bark beetle

Bark beetles of the Scolytidae family feed and breed between bark and wood, frequently engraving both with their network of tunnels. Eight or more different kinds of these tiny beetles feed in weakened, dying, or dead larch. The two most common species are the eastern larch beetle, *Dendroctonus simplex* LeConte, which feeds exclusively on larch, and the four-eyed spruce bark beetle □, *Polygraphus rufipennis* (Kirby), which feeds on a number of conifers. When both are present on standing trees, the larger eastern larch beetle is found more frequently on the lower part of the stem and the other is found on the upper part. Because of similarity in all stages of development, the identification of bark beetles is best left to specialists.

The eastern larch beetle □ is treated here as an example. It overwinters mainly in the adult stage. The adults, about 4 mm long, emerge from the bark in May and, on finding suitable breeding mate-

Eastern larch beetle

rial, bore directly through the bark. Their attack on living material is marked by a flow of resin and dark brown boring dust. The wide tunnels, called galleries, in which the eggs are laid, are mostly in the bark, and the wood is only slightly scored. The larvae □ complete development there in about a month and then change to the pupal and adult stages in the succeeding month. The parent adults leave and construct a second set of egg galleries in suitable material and a second brood develops to the adult stage that summer. A third brood is often initiated in other material, but these individuals usually do not develop beyond the larval stage that year. Parent beetles usually die in the third brood gallery.

Removal of dead or dying timber from a forest stand will prevent the development of destructive populations there. Control of bark beetles in individual shade trees is seldom warranted, because the tree is usually seriously weakened by other factors before the beetles arrive on the scene.

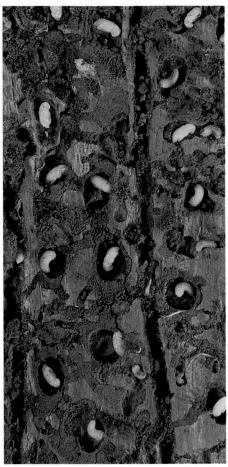

Larvae and pupae in tunnels

# Ambrosia beetles

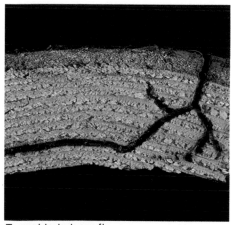
Tunnel in balsam fir

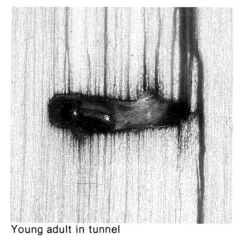
Young adult in tunnel

Ambrosia beetle damage is characterized by a circular tunnel that goes directly through the bark and into the wood □. Moreover, the walls of tunnels and the adjacent wood are stained black by the fungus on which the beetles feed. Tunnels usually occur in the outer wood of logs, are free of boring dust, and may be simple or branched. These beetles will attack and survive only in unseasoned wood; with a decrease in the moisture content of the wood, development stops. The tunnels of ambrosia beetles cause no lessening of structural soundness of the wood, but the stain may be undesirable.

The life history of the striped ambrosia beetle, *Trypodendron lineatum* (Oliv.), is typical for the group. Adult emergence from hibernation sites occurs soon after the snow has gone. Male and female beetles work together constructing the galleries. The eggs are laid in niches, in the tunnel branches which sometimes follow annual rings, and the larvae, on hatching, extend the niche to form a cradle where development is completed. The young adults □ leave to find hibernation sites. The original pair of adults may have two to three broods in different breeding material in the first year and may produce additional broods in the succeeding year.

For control measures against ambrosia beetles in the forest, the appropriate Research Centre of the Canadian Forestry Service should be consulted (see page 10). Beetles will not infest stored wood with bark removed, and any beetles around homes, emerging from structural material are a nuisance only.

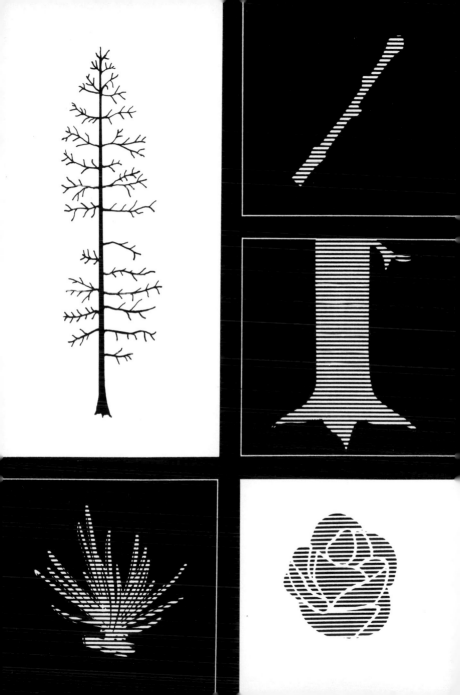

# Larch – cone

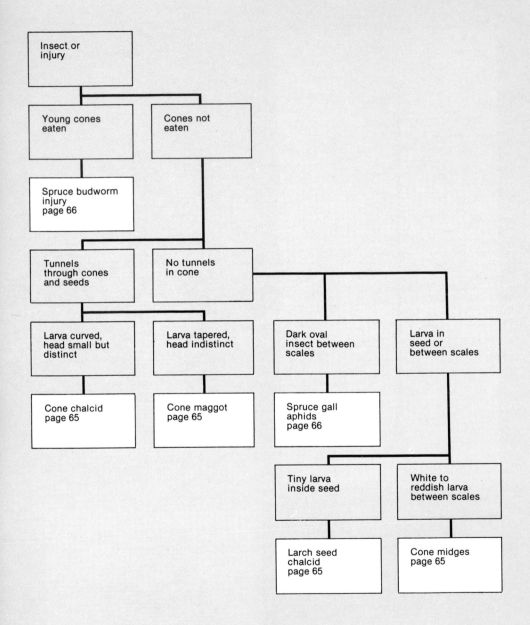

Insect or injury

Young cones eaten

Cones not eaten

Spruce budworm injury page 66

Tunnels through cones and seeds

No tunnels in cone

Larva curved, head small but distinct

Larva tapered, head indistinct

Dark oval insect between scales

Larva in seed or between scales

Cone chalcid page 65

Cone maggot page 65

Spruce gall aphids page 66

Tiny larva inside seed

White to reddish larva between scales

Larch seed chalcid page 65

Cone midges page 65

# Cone insects

Larch seed chalcid adult

Larch seed chalcid larva

Relatively little is known about insects in the cones of larch. A number of different species have been found in Ontario: one feeds inside the seed, two burrow in the cones and feed on the seeds, several species live between the scales, and others, normally foliage feeders, sometimes eat tender young cones.

The larch seed chalcid, *Megastigmus laricis* Marcovitch, is a very tiny insect □ and the larva completes its development within a single seed □. The larva of the cone chalcid □ is much larger than that of the seed chalcid: it appears to burrow through the cone and feed on the seeds. The cone maggot □, *Hylemya* species, also burrows through the cone from seed to seed. A number of cone midges of the family Cecidomyidae feed between the cone scales; one species, *Lestodiplosis grassator* (Fyles), is probably predaceous on other cone insects. Midge larvae are orange □ or white and taper from the middle to both ends.

Cone chalcid larva

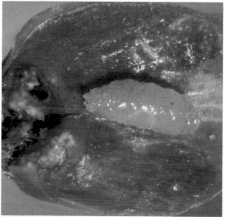

Cone maggot

Cone damage by spruce budworm

Spruce gall aphids that have larch as an alternate host are also often found between cone scales on larch (see page 45).

Foliage feeders such as the spruce budworm and the larch needleworm will sometimes feed on tender young cones □.

For further information on control of cone insects, the advice of specialists should be sought through the appropriate Research Centre listed on page 10.

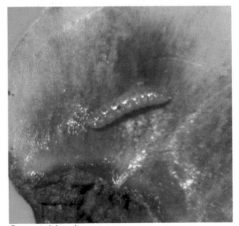

Cone midge larva

# Cedar

*Also see *discoloured foliage* on page 94.

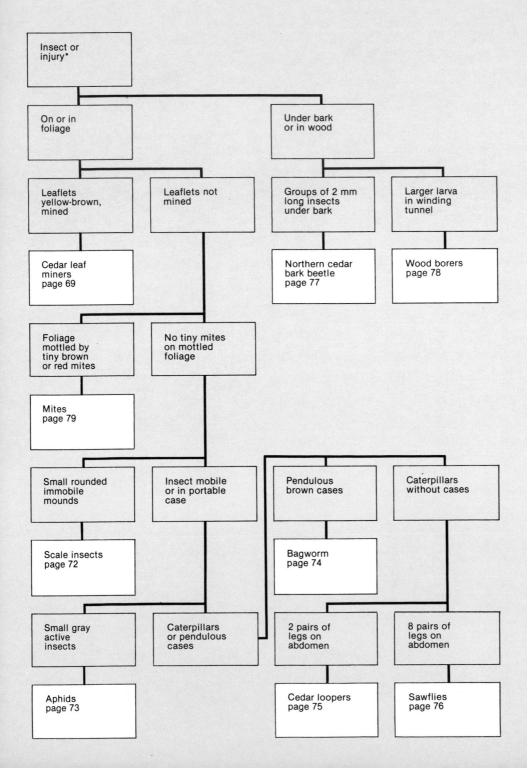

Insect or injury*

On or in foliage

Under bark or in wood

Leaflets yellow-brown, mined

Leaflets not mined

Groups of 2 mm long insects under bark

Larger larva in winding tunnel

Cedar leaf miners page 69

Northern cedar bark beetle page 77

Wood borers page 78

Foliage mottled by tiny brown or red mites

No tiny mites on mottled foliage

Mites page 79

Small rounded immobile mounds

Insect mobile or in portable case

Pendulous brown cases

Caterpillars without cases

Scale insects page 72

Bagworm page 74

Small gray active insects

Caterpillars or pendulous cases

2 pairs of legs on abdomen

8 pairs of legs on abdomen

Aphids page 73

Cedar loopers page 75

Sawflies page 76

# Cedar leaf miners

Damaged trees

• Body of larva green; pupa in mined leaflet, green, curved at tip ................... *Argyresthia thuiella* (Packard)
• Body of larva green; pupa on foliage in a white silken cocoon ................... *Argyresthia aureoargentella* Brower
• Body of larva green; pupa on foliage in a brown-flecked cocoon ................... *Argyresthia canadensis* Freeman
• Body of larva brown; pupa in mined leaflet, brown, not curved at tip ................ *Pulicalvaria thujaella* (Kearfott)

The cedar leaf miners, also called arbor-vitae leaf miners, are common pests of cedar in eastern Canada and the northeastern United States. Although *A. thuiella* is perhaps the most common species in Ontario, it is not uncommon to find all four species in a single location. Feeding by these insects has caused severe "scorching" of the foliage □ and often subsequent twig, branch, or tree kill in

Mined foliage

New foliage

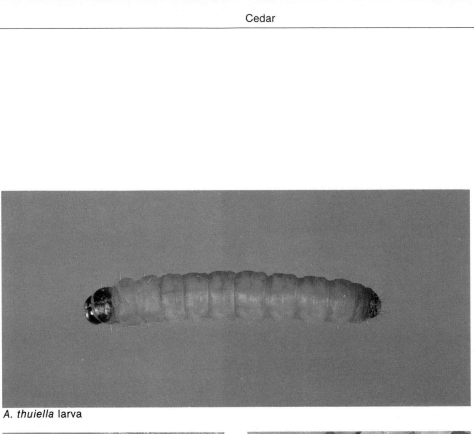

*A. thuiella* larva

*A. thuiella* pupa exposed

*A. aureoargentella* cocoon

*A. canadensis* cocoon

*P. thujaella* pupa exposed

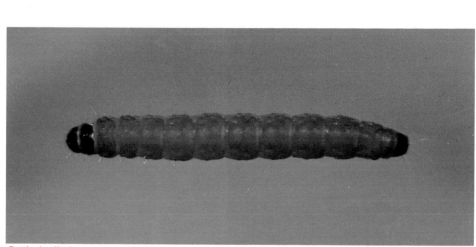

*P. thujaella* larva

southern Ontario, Quebec, New Brunswick, and Prince Edward Island. Fortunately, however, severely injured trees will often produce new foliage ☐ later in the growing season.

These leaf miners overwinter on the tree in hollowed out yellow-brown leaflets, the *Argyresthia* species as nearly full-grown larvae and the *Pulicalvaria* as younger larvae. Mining is completed in the spring, causing discolored foliage ☐, and the full-grown larvae are 6 or 7 mm long.

The larva of *A. thuiella* ☐ changes to a pupa in the mined leaflet. The curved posterior tip and green color of the pupa ☐ are characteristic for the species. The larvae of *A. aureoargentella* and *A. canadensis* are similar in appearance to the larva of *A. thuiella*. However, they vacate the mined leaflet and change to pupae in silken cocoons attached to the foliage ☐, ☐. In Ontario, adults of the *Argyresthia* species emerge from late May to early July.

The brown larva of *P. thujaella* ☐ also changes to a pupa in the mined leaflet ☐, but this pupa is brown and the tip is not curved. The adults of this species emerge a few weeks later than the *Argyresthia* species.

Although parasites often kill many larvae of the cedar leaf miners, other controls may become necessary. In Ontario, a systemic insecticide would be effective if applied in early May or mid-August. On individual ornamentals the infested twig tips can be pruned and destroyed in early spring.

# Scale insects

Fletcher scale

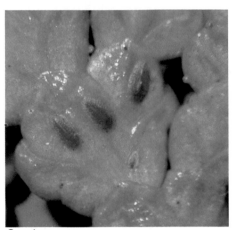

Crawlers

Scale insects are unusual in that the adult females are immobile, with no appendages showing. The males, which are seldom seen, are winged and only about 1 mm long. Scale insects insert their slender feeding tubes through the bark and feed on sap drawn from a wide variety of trees and shrubs. Heavily infested trees and shrubs lose their color and have thin foliage. Although a number of species attack cedar and juniper, the following two are most common.

The Fletcher scale, *Lecanium fletcheri* Cockerell, occurs on cedar and juniper but perhaps more often on yew. In Ontario, it overwinters as a partly grown nymph on the twigs. The nymphs become active again in late April and early May. In June they settle on the twigs, where they soon assume the shape of the adult scale □. Small whitish eggs are deposited in large numbers beneath the adult scale. Soon after the eggs hatch, the young, flat, oval "crawlers" □ settle on the leaves, where they insert their fine feeding tubes in the leaf and feed until the latter part of September, when they move to the twigs to overwinter.

The juniper scale, *Carulaspis (carueli) juniperi* (Bouché), is a small circular scale, white in color with a raised yellow center. Junipers, especially the ornamental varieties, are occasionally heavily damaged, but cedars are also attacked. In Ontario the mature scale overwinters. Eggs are present under the scale in June and the "crawlers" are active in July.

If control measures become necessary on ornamentals, a dormant oil may be applied in early spring. Contact or systemic insecticides recommended for scale insects are effective against the crawler stage.

# Aphids

A number of species of aphid belonging to the *Cinara* group are found on cedar and juniper. The only one known to occur on eastern white cedar in Ontario is *C. cupressi* (Buckton). It has not caused serious injury to date. The black eggs □, typical of the many members of this group, overwinter on the tree. The gray aphids □ feed throughout the summer on sap drawn from the leaflets or twigs.

*C. juniperi* (de Geer) □ is usually a solitary feeder on shoots and twigs of common juniper in Ontario. In the eastern United States, *C. sabinae* (Gillette & Palmer) has been reported in large numbers on red cedar. It is a reddish-brown aphid about 3 mm long, covered with a white powdery substance. When it is abundant, black mold usually develops on excretions of the insect, making the tree unsightly. Further information on the *Cinara* group of aphids is given on page 53.

For control, an insecticide recommended for aphids should be used.

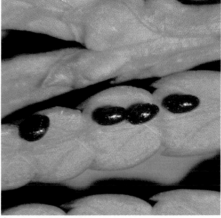
*Cinara* aphid eggs

Colony of cedar aphids

Juniper aphid

# Bagworm

The bagworm, *Thyridopteryx ephemeraeformis* (Haworth), is widely distributed in the eastern United States and is occasionally found in Ontario. It feeds on a wide variety of trees but appears to prefer cedar and juniper in Ontario, where it is found mainly in urban areas. The insect derives its name from the bag-like case □ that is built and carried around by the larva.

The eggs overwinter in the bags on the tree or shrub and hatch in late spring. The young larvae start to feed immediately and to construct bags, using copious amounts of silk with bits of leaf and twig. As the larva feeds, only the head and the thoracic legs protrude from the open end of the finished bag. In the fall, when the larva is full grown, it attaches its bag to a twig with silk and then changes to a pupa. The bags are 25 mm or more in length. In about three weeks the pupa changes to an adult moth. The female is bizarre, maggot-like, and wingless with a yellow-white body, naked except for a circle of hairs at the posterior end. The male is sooty black, winged, and densely hairy. After mating, the female lays her eggs in the bag, where they overwinter.

Control can be effected by handpicking and destroying the bags while the insects are inside. A systemic or stomach insecticide would also be appropriate if required.

Bag on cedar

# Cedar loopers

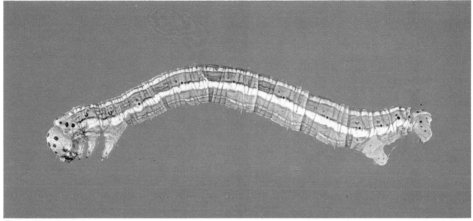

False hemlock looper

A number of different kinds of looper may be found on cedar, but their feeding is usually not of serious consequence. One of these, the hemlock looper, *Lambdina fiscellaria fiscellaria* (Guenée), also feeds on larch and is illustrated on page 37. Three other common species are briefly described here.

The false hemlock looper □, *Nepytia canosaria* (Walker), feeds on a number of conifers, including cedar, mainly from June to August. Full-grown larvae are about 25 mm long. Eggs are laid in small clusters on the bark, where they overwinter.

Two kinds of looper that feed almost exclusively on cedar are *Semiothisa orillata* (Walker) □ and *Eupithecia gibsonata* Taylor. Their distribution in eastern North America probably coincides with that of eastern white cedar. The larvae of both species are very similar, and are 20 mm or less in length. They may be found from early July to late September. Both overwinter as pupae on the ground. Epidemics of

*S. orillata* larva

these insects are unknown.

If loopers become abundant on ornamentals, they should be hand-picked and destroyed, or sprayed before they are full grown with a contact or stomach insecticide recommended for caterpillars.

# Sawflies

Larva on cedar

Larva on juniper

Two or more species of the sawfly genus *Monoctenus* feed on the foliage of cedar and juniper in eastern North America. They seldom cause noticeable injury and, because they are solitary feeders, they are rarely noticed. The larvae feed from June to September and, when full grown, are about 18 mm long □, □. In the fall they drop to the ground and spin cocoons, in which they overwinter. The larvae change to pupae and subsequently to adult sawflies in the spring.

Control measures have not been required for the cedar and juniper sawflies. If they should become numerous on hedges or ornamentals, a contact or stomach insecticide recommended for sawflies should be used.

# Northern cedar bark beetle

The northern cedar bark beetle, *Phloeosinus canadensis* Swaine, is probably the only bark beetle breeding in cedar and juniper. It attacks damaged, weakened, or dying trees and its presence is indicated by the fine rust-colored boring dust □. Beetles may be found under the bark □ in all parts of the tree from the small twigs to the heavy-barked trunk. When high populations result from abundant breeding material, adult feeding on twigs and leaves often causes flagging and browning of foliage on nearby healthy trees.

There is apparently one generation each year. The breeding gallery □ under the bark runs with the grain and is mostly in the wood. The eggs are closely spaced in deep niches along the side. On hatching, the larvae initially construct narrow tunnels that run laterally and then diverge as the tunnels widen to accommodate larger larvae and pupae.

No control measures are known and it is unlikely that any will be warranted. In ornamental plantings, potential breeding material such as dead or dying branches or stems should be removed and destroyed.

Boring dust

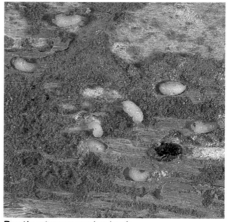
Beetle stages under bark

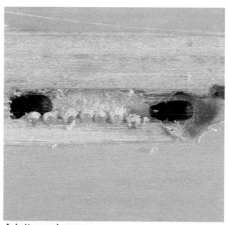
Adults and eggs

# Wood borers

Larva in pupal chamber

Adult

Tunnels on wood surface

A number of different kinds of borers feed in dead or dying cedar and juniper trees. The cedar tree borer, *Semanotus ligneus ligneus* (Fabricius), is used as an example here. The adults ☐ emerge from their tunnels in May. After selecting suitable material, the females lay their eggs in slits cut in the bark. The larvae soon emerge from the eggs and feed throughout the first summer between the bark and wood, creating tortuous tunnels ☐ mostly in the wood. The first winter is spent in these shallow tunnels. The larvae continue feeding throughout the second summer until they are full grown and about 25 mm long. At this time they tunnel through oval holes ☐ into the sapwood, where they prepare chambers in which to change to pupae. Later in the fall the pupae change to adult beetles that remain in the tunnel chambers until the following spring.

Damage to cedar and juniper has not been sufficiently serious to warrant control measures.

# Mites

Cedar damage by spruce spider mite

A number of mite species are found on cedar and juniper in North America, but by far the most common one in Ontario is the spruce spider mite, *Oligonychus ununguis* (Jacobi). Although difficult to see with the naked eye, it is nevertheless capable of causing considerable damage to ornamental trees and shrubs. These dark-colored mites feed by sucking sap from the leaves and, when abundant, cause mottling of the leaves ☐ and eventually early shedding of foliage. As they move about, they spin fine silk over the foliage surface, and the trapped dust and debris heighten the unhealthy appearance. Five to eight generations of these mites can develop during a hot, dry summer, building up incredible numbers. The spider mite overwinters in the egg stage. Additional information on this species may be found in *Insects of Eastern Spruces, Fir and Hemlock,* Forestry Technical Report 23, an earlier handbook in this series.

False spider mite on cedar

False spider mite on juniper

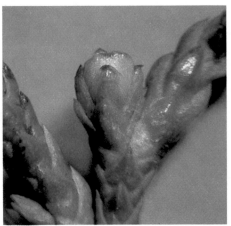

Bud mite on juniper

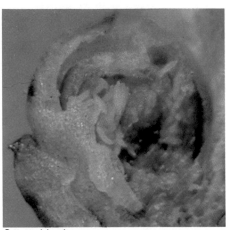

Opened bud

Two species of false spider mites also occur on cedar and juniper in Canada, and available records indicate that they occur widely in North America. These mites are bright red and have the general shape and size of a spider mite. *Pentamerismus canadensis* MacGregor kills leaflets on cedar □ whereas *P. erythreus* (Ewing) □, though found on both cedar and juniper, has not caused noticeable damage in Ontario. Little is known about the life history of these two species of false spider mites.

Two other species of mites occasionally found on juniper and cedar are microscopic, worm-like, four-legged creatures as opposed to the typical eight-legged mites. *Trisetacus thujivagrans* Smith is a bud mite that kills shoot tips of juniper □, □ and it has also been found on cedar. The pile mite, *Eriophyes* species, causes the development of a pile-like growth on juniper foliage □. Both of these species are apparently rare and little is known about their life

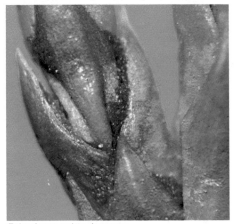

*Eriophyes* mite damage

history.

If control measures become necessary for any mite on ornamental plants, a miticide should be used.

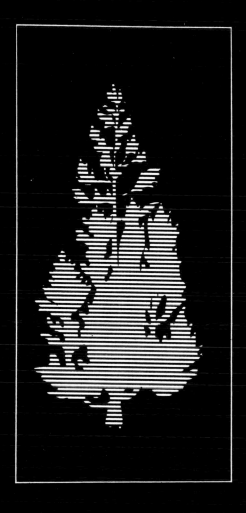

# Juniper*

*Eastern red cedar, technically
a juniper, is included here

**If insects or their injury are
not found, see *discolored
foliage,* page 94

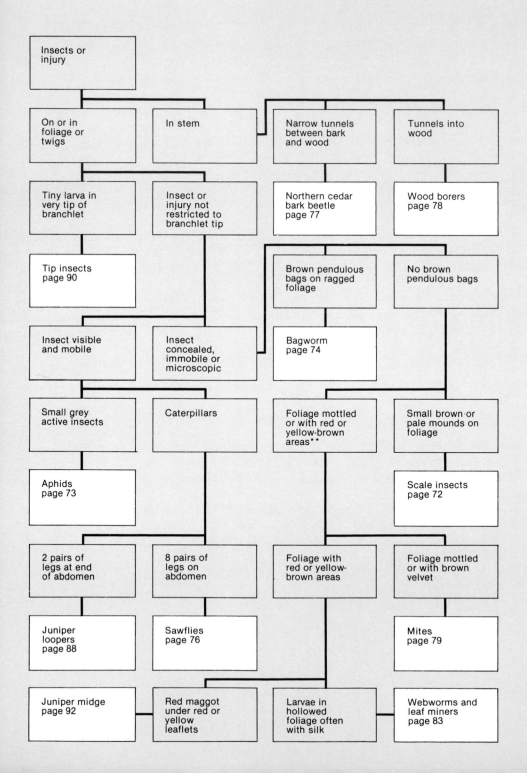

# Webworms and leaf miners

* Material used for illustrations, courtesy of Maritimes Forest Research Centre.

• Larvae brown, striped or plain; gregarious in nests of dead needles, webbing and excreta . . . . . Juniper webworms
• Larvae green, pinkish or brown; solitary in hollow yellow branchlets, sometimes with silk and excreta . . . . . Juniper leaf miners, page 84

## Juniper webworms

Two kinds of webworms, both accidentally introduced to this continent, cause browning of foliage on common and ornamental juniper in southern Canada and the northern United States. The moths of the juniper webworm, *Dichomeris marginella* Denis & Schiffermüller, fly in June and July and lay their eggs in leaf axils of new growth. As the eggs hatch, the tiny larvae mine needles that later turn brown and die.* The dead needles are incorporated into a web spun between branchlets and become noticeable on the foliage by early August □. The larvae feed until late fall and overwinter in silken cases in the webbed foliage. Feeding is resumed in the spring. The full-grown larva is about 14 mm long with a light brown body and darker longitudinal stripes □. In early summer the larvae change to pupae in whitish silk cases in the webbed foliage.

The pale juniper webworm, *Aethes (= Phalonia) rutilana* (Hübner), apparently feeds mainly on the common juniper shrub. In Ontario the moths fly in late July and early August. The larvae mine nee-

Damage by juniper webworm

Mature larva

applied in early spring.

**Juniper leaf miners**

Because of limited study of juniper insects, little is known about juniper leaf miners. Information on the occurrence of the moth stage is lacking.

**• On common juniper**
In late summer and early fall, the larva of *Pulicalvaria gibsonella* (Kearfott) ties the terminal needles into a bundle and mines or hollows them out from the concave side □. It overwinters in a silken tube inside the bundle. In the spring the larva moves to the new growth, where it webs and feeds on the terminal needles. When full grown, in late May or early June, and about 7 mm long, the larva □ changes to a pupa in the feeding site.

The young larva of *Argyresthia annettella* Busck also starts mining the needles in midsummer. It tunnels from the base of the needle toward the apex and passes through the shoot from one needle base to the next. After overwintering in the tunnel, it continues feeding in the same manner in the spring. The full-grown larva, probably a greenish color, leaves the tunnel in May and changes to a pupa in an open-mesh, silk cocoon □ on the foliage.

A third species, and there may be others, is *Coleotechnites (Recurvaria) juniperella* (Kearfott), reported from the northeastern United States.

Damage by pale juniper webworm

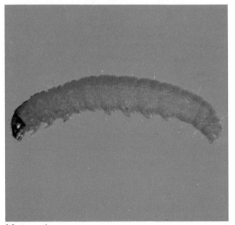
Mature larva

dles throughout late summer and fall, and overwinter in silk-lined, excreta covered cases attached to the twigs □. Feeding is resumed in the spring when the larva hollows out the needles from the concave surface. The full-grown larva is yellow-brown and about 11 mm long □. The larvae change to pupae from late May to early July.

Juniper webworms on ornamental shrubs can be controlled with a contact or stomach insecticide recommended for caterpillars and

Cocoon – *A. annettella*

Tip damaged by *P. gibsonella*

### • On eastern red cedar

The larva of *Argyresthia freyella* Walsingham overwinters in the hollowed out scale-like leaves. After feeding in the shoot tips □ for a short period in the spring, the larva is full grown □, and about 7 mm long. It changes to a pupa, in a spindle-shaped white cocoon with light brown mottling, on the foliage outside the mine □. The moths fly from late May to early July. A little-known species, *A. affinis* Braun, feeds in a manner similar to that of the preceding species. It probably changes to a green, somewhat curled pupa in the larval tunnel.

The larva of *Eucordylea albicostata* Freeman tunnels in the scale-like leaves starting near the base of a branchlet and mining towards the tip □. It overwinters in the tunnel and resumes feeding in the spring. When the larva is full grown □, about the end of May, it changes to a pupa in a cocoon of silk and excreta, spun on the foliage.

Mature larva

Cocoon – *A. freyella*

The species *Coleotechnites (Recurvaria) juniperella* (Kearfott) has also been reported mining the leaves of eastern red cedar in the northeastern United States.

## • Control
A systemic insecticide would be effective against young larvae of any of the species of leaf miners on juniper.

Damage by *A. freyella*

Mature larva – *A. freyella*

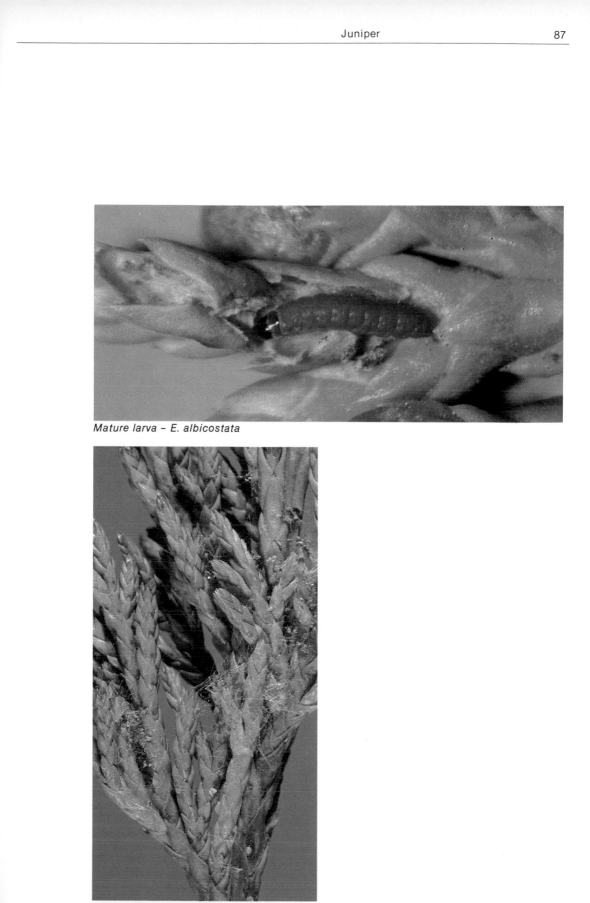

*Mature larva – E. albicostata*

Damage by *E. albicostata*

# Juniper loopers

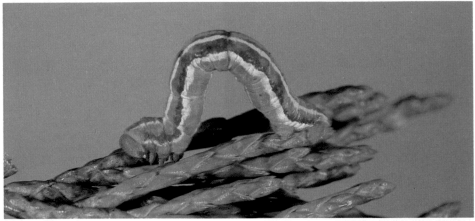
Mature *Thera* larva

Two groups of loopers in the genera *Thera* and *Eupithecia* feed on juniper, occasionally causing severe browning of the foliage. The feeding injury is particularly unsightly on specimen shrubs and foundation plantings □.

In the first group, three species of *Thera* occur in North America. The larvae are similar for all three and, when full grown, are about 17 mm long. The larvae of *T. otisi* Dyar feed from late May to late August in Alberta and southeastern British Columbia. Two species, *T. contracta* Packard and *T. juniperata* Linnaeus, occur in eastern Canada and the northeastern United States. Both overwinter on the foliage in the egg stage. In Ontario the larvae of *juniperata* □ feed from June to October. The larvae change to pupae in the fall near the feeding sites or on the ground under the shrubs. The moth adults □ emerge from the pupal cases from September to early October and lay their eggs on the foliage. The life cycle of *contracta* is similar to that

Adult

of the preceding species. However, the moths are apparently in flight much earlier – mainly from late July to September.

In the second group, *E. sobrinata interruptofasciata* Packard □ occurs throughout eastern North America. Winter is spent in the egg stage and the larvae feed from May to July. Full-grown larvae are about 13 mm long. The moths fly from late August to mid-October. Another species in this group, *E. arceuthata* Freyer, has a transconti-

Mature *Eupithecia* larva

nental range. Pupae overwinter and
the moths fly in June and July. The
larvae, which are similar to those
of the preceding species, feed
from mid-July to mid-September
and, when full grown, are about
15 mm long.

For control of any of these loopers, a contact or stomach insecticide recommended for caterpillars
should be applied when the larvae
are small.

Damaged tree

# Tip insects

• Yellowish or reddish larva, wide at middle, tapering to both ends; head capsule not apparent . . . . . . . Juniper tip midges
• White larva, wide at thorax, tapering posteriorly; head capsule present though small . . . . . . . . . . . . Juniper tip gall chalcid

## Juniper tip midges

A number of midges in the genus *Oligotrophus* feed inside the tips of juniper twigs. Apparently, these insects are not common in Canada, but they have been reported from nurseries in the northern United States. Feeding by the larvae of these midges has resulted in unsightly dead tips on nursery stock ☐. In Ontario, small numbers of larvae have been found in tips of naturally growing eastern red cedar.

The larva overwinters in a small chamber in a branchlet tip. In the spring, when the larva is full grown and about 0.75 mm long, it changes to a pupa inside the larval chamber. In a few weeks the adult midges, small, delicate mosquito-like insects, emerge from the pupal cases. After mating, the female lays her eggs on the new foliage. As the larvae emerge from the eggs they crawl to the branchlet tips and enter the central cavity of a growing tip. Each larva remains in this cavity throughout its entire feeding period. Four generations of these midges in a year have been reported in Ohio. The number of generations in Ontario is not known.

Tip midge damage

If control of juniper tip midges becomes necessary, a systemic insecticide applied in late May should be effective.

## Juniper tip gall chalcid

The tip gall chalcid, *Rhopalicus* species, has been found in considerable numbers on eastern red cedar in Ontario, yet it causes little noticeable injury. The species has also been reported from Ohio. Injury by this chalcid is very similar to that caused by the tip midge in that only the very tip of the branchlets is affected.

The chalcid overwinters as an immature larva in the swollen tip gall □. The larva is white □, tapering to the last abdominal segment, which bears a long spine-like tail that is slightly curved. When disturbed, the larva reacts by quickly rotating the abdomen in a circular motion. When it is full grown and about 1 mm long, the larva changes to a pupa in the gall. The pupa is entirely dull black. The tiny brilliantly colored adult □ soon emerges from the pupa and the female lays her eggs on the new foliage. Two or three generations a year are reported in Ohio.

Control has not been required for the tip gall chalcid, but if it should become necessary a systemic insecticide, applied in early spring, would be appropriate.

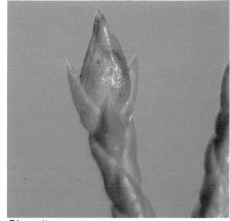

*Rhopalicus* gall

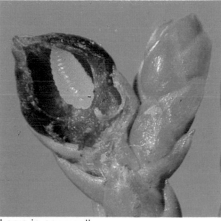

Larva in open gall

Adult

# Juniper midge

The juniper midge, *Contarinia juniperina* Felt, probably occurs throughout much of the range of eastern red cedar in North America. The insect has been reported on many kinds of juniper in the United States but in Ontario is known only on eastern red cedar. Tips on injured trees turn brown during June and July as a result of midge feeding during the previous summer. Serious injury by the midge has not been recorded in Canada.

The larvae apparently overwinter in the feeding site, a reddish or yellow blister at a needle base □, or in the ground under the tree. The full-grown larva □ is about 2 mm long, bright orange and spindle-shaped. In spring the larvae change to pupae in the ground, and the adult midges □ emerge from late May to July. After mating, the females lay their eggs on juniper foliage near the branch tips. When the eggs hatch, the larvae bore into the branchlets, where they feed throughout the summer. Some may complete their feeding and drop to the ground in the fall, but it seems that in Ontario the majority overwinter in the foliage.

If control of the juniper midge becomes necessary, a systemic insecticide should be applied at two- to three-week intervals starting in late June.

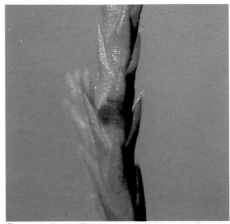
Damaged needle

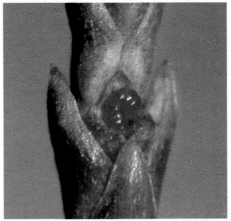
Exposed larva

Adult midge

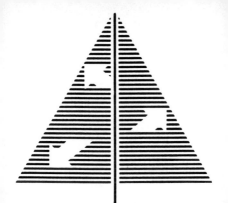

# Discolored foliage

Juniper winterkill

Herbicide injury to larch

Weevil larva

Natural browning of cedar

Sometimes foliage of branches or even of the entire tree turns yellow to brown although no obvious cause of injury can be found. This may be caused by root-feeding insects such as the C-shaped whitish larvae of weevils in the genera *Hylobius, Phyllobius* and *Otiorhynchus* □. Foliage discoloration may also be caused by changes in soil levels, water levels, soil compaction, soil contamination, or disease organisms. Cedar and juniper plantings are particularly susceptible to damage known as "winterkill" □ which is characterized by tips of twigs or entire shrubs turning yellow or brown in early spring. This discoloration results from unfavorable winter weather conditions or lack of hardiness. In the fall, however, when the oldest branchlets on cedar – those nearest the trunk – turn rusty red □, there is no cause for alarm. A natural phenomenon is occurring: the trees are shedding their oldest foliage. When needles of larch turn yellow in summer with no evidence of insect feeding the cause may be environmental disturbances or herbicides □; in the latter instance there is distortion of the new growth. Larch needles turn yellow in late fall □ before shedding; the only native conifer which sheds all its needles annually.

Fall color of larch

# Index

# Acknowledgments

**Environment Canada**

| | |
|---|---|
| Photography | E.R. Rayner, P. Montgrain, W.J. Miller |
| Cover Photo | O.H. Lindquist and A.H. Rose |
| Artwork | P. Jakibchuk |
| Editing & Production | W.K. Robins and A. Lavallée |

# Metric/English conversion scales

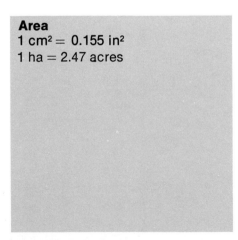

**Linear**

| Metres | Feet |
|---|---|
| 1 | 2½ |
| 2 | 5 |
| 3 | 10 |
| 4 | |
| 5 | |
| 6 | 20 |
| 7 | |
| 8 | |
| 9 | 30 |
| 10 | |

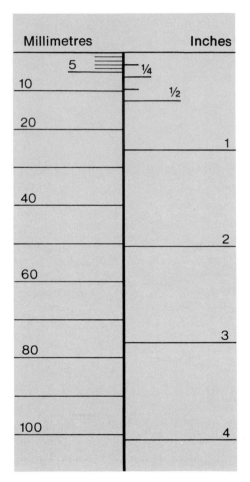

| Millimetres | Inches |
|---|---|
| 5 | ¼ |
| 10 | ½ |
| 20 | |
| | 1 |
| 40 | |
| | 2 |
| 60 | |
| | 3 |
| 80 | |
| 100 | 4 |

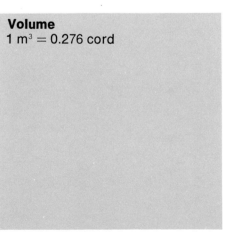

**Area**
1 cm² = 0.155 in²
1 ha = 2.47 acres

**Volume**
1 m³ = 0.276 cord

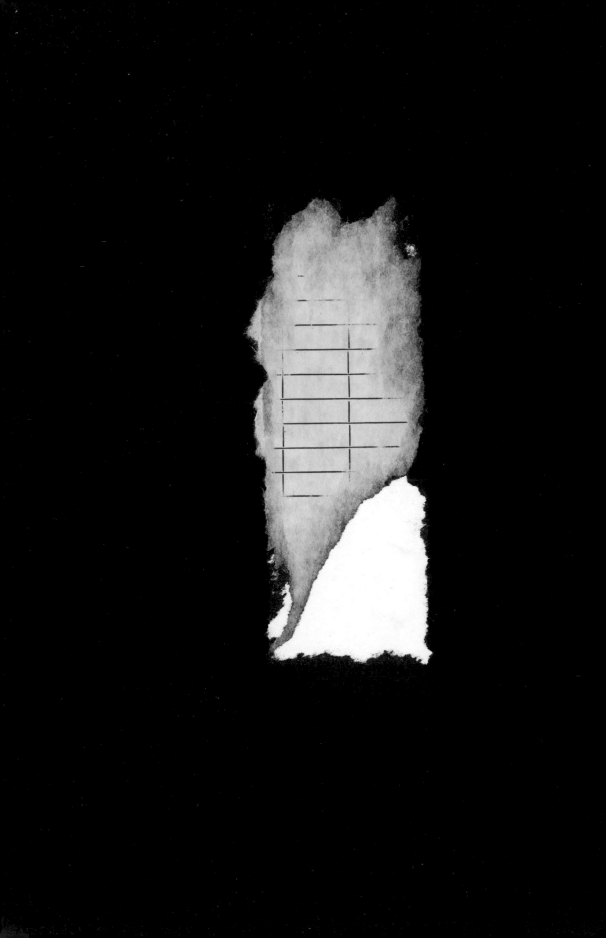